First Edition

W9-ANG-277

triumphlearning™
Common Core Coach
Mathematics 1

D1372745

Dr. Jerry Kaplan
Senior Mathematics Consultant

Common Core Coach, Mathematics, First Edition, Grade 1   T212NA   ISBN-13: 978-1-61997-998-7
Cover Illustration: Scott Burroughs/Deborah Wolfe LTD.

Triumph Learning® 136 Madison Avenue, 7th Floor, New York, NY 10016

Contents

Problem Solving · Fluency Lesson · Performance Task

Common Core
State Standards

Domain 1
Operations and Algebraic Thinking

Domain 1
Operations and Algebraic Thinking

How many players are at the game?

Problem Solving: Addition

★ You can **add** to solve some word problems.

Example 1

How many erasers in all?

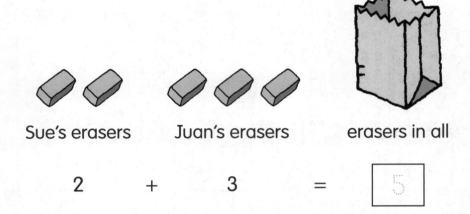

Sue's erasers	Juan's erasers	erasers in all

$$2 \quad + \quad 3 \quad = \quad \boxed{5}$$

▶ There are _____ erasers in all.

Example 2

How many marbles in all?

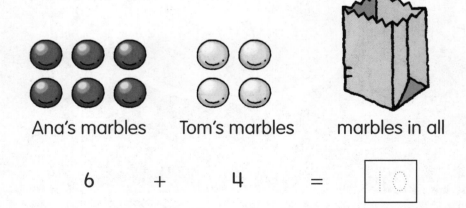

Ana's marbles	Tom's marbles	marbles in all

$$6 \quad + \quad 4 \quad = \quad \boxed{10}$$

▶ There are _____ marbles in all.

Example 3

How many blocks are in the bag?

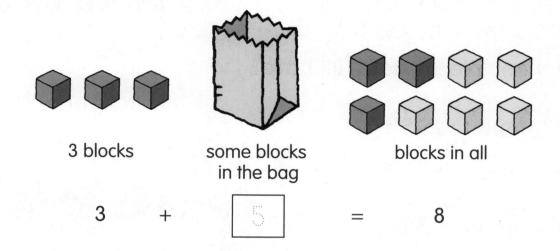

3 blocks   some blocks   blocks in all
                 in the bag

$3 \quad + \quad \boxed{5} \quad = \quad 8$

▶ There are _____ blocks in the bag.

Example 4

Start with 9 blocks.
Then add 7 more.
How many blocks in all?

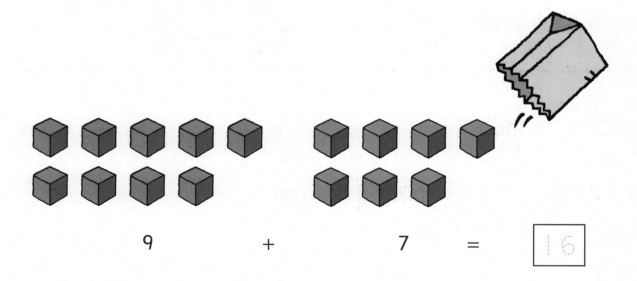

$9 \quad + \quad 7 \quad = \quad \boxed{16}$

▶ There are _____ blocks in all.

Bill has 5 puzzle pieces.

Jill has 3 more pieces than Bill.

How many pieces does Jill have?

Find 3 more than 5.

1

I more than 5 is _____ 6 _____.

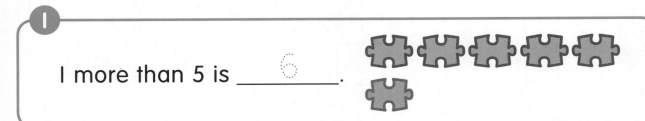

2

2 more than 5 is _____.

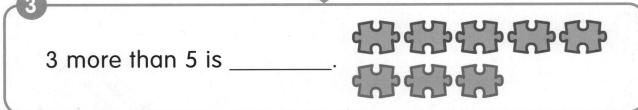

3

3 more than 5 is _____.

So 3 more than 5 is _____.

▶ Jill has _____ puzzle pieces.

Practice

1 Hyun has 4 red blocks. Her mom gives her 7 blue blocks. How many blocks does Hyun have in all?

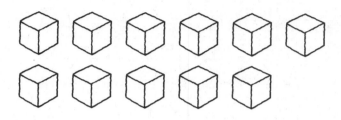

4 + 7 = ☐

Hyun has _____ blocks in all.

....

2 There are 5 green toy trucks and some yellow toy trucks. There are 13 toy trucks in all. How many yellow toy trucks are there?

5 + ☐ = 13

There are _____ yellow toy trucks.

3 Rosa had some gold stars. Dad gave her 6 more. Then she had 15 gold stars. How many gold stars did Rosa have to start?

$$\boxed{} + 6 = 15$$

Rosa had _____ gold stars to start.

....

4 Sam has 3 more stickers than Jim has. Jim has 10 stickers. How many stickers does Sam have?

Jim's stickers

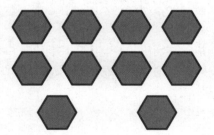

$$10 + 3 = \boxed{}$$

Sam has _____ stickers.

5 **DRAW** There are 7 red balloons and 5 yellow balloons at the party. How many balloons are there in all?

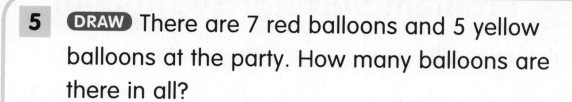

$7 + 5 = \boxed{}$

There are _____ balloons in all.

How did you find your answer?

Talk about it.

Problem Solving: Subtraction

★ You can **subtract** to solve some word problems.

Example 1

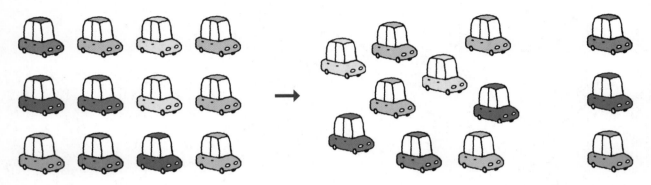

12 cars parked.   9 cars drove away.

How many cars are parked now?

12 − 9 = ⬚ 3

▶ There are _____ cars parked now.

Example 2

There were 9 boats.   Some boats sailed away.   There were 5 boats left.

How many boats sailed away?

9 − ⬚ 4 = 5

▶ _____ boats sailed away.

Example 3

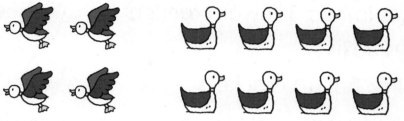

? Some ducks were in the lake.

4 ducks flew away.

Now 8 ducks are left.

How many ducks were in the lake to start?

$$\boxed{12} - 4 = 8$$

▶ There were _____ ducks in the lake to start.

Example 4

There are 13 peppers. There are 7 red peppers.
The rest are green.

How many green peppers are there?

$$13 - 7 = \boxed{6}$$

▶ There are _____ green peppers.

Robin has 3 fewer crackers than Nick.

Nick has 10 crackers.

How many crackers does Robin have?

Find 3 fewer than 10.

1

1 fewer than 10 is _____9_____.

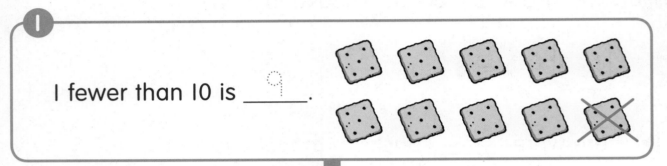

2

2 fewer than 10 is _____.

3

3 fewer than 10 is _____.

So 3 fewer than 10 is _____.

▶ Robin has _____ crackers.

Practice

1 Zoe has 13 buttons. She has 9 green buttons.
The rest are yellow.
How many yellow buttons are there?

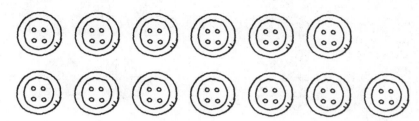

$13 - 9 = \boxed{}$

There are _____ yellow buttons.

---

2 Sophie has 3 fewer stamps than Mike.
Mike has 9 stamps.
How many stamps does Sophie have?

Mike's stamps

$9 - 3 = \boxed{}$

Sophie has _____ stamps.

3 There were some toys on the table.

Lily put 2 toys away.

Now there are 5 toys on the table.

How many toys were on the table to start?

?

$$\boxed{} - 2 = 5$$

There were _____ toys on the table to start.

....

4 Adam had 12 pencils. He gave some away.

He has 8 pencils left.

How many pencils did Adam give away?

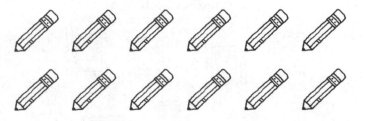

$$12 - \boxed{} = 8$$

Adam gave away _____ pencils.

5 **DRAW** There were 17 flowers in a garden. Dan cut 8 flowers. How many flowers are left?

$17 - 8 = \boxed{}$

There are _____ flowers left.

How did you find your answer?

Talk about it.

Problem Solving: Adding Three Numbers

★ You can add three numbers to solve some problems.

Example 1

Tim has 5 toys. Jane has 2 toys and Sally has 4 toys.
How many toys are there in all?

      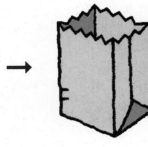

Tim's toys		Jane's toys		Sally's toys		toys in all
5	+	2	+	4	=	

 Put Tim's and Jane's toys together.
$5 + 2 = 7$

 Add Sally's toys to find how many toys in all.

$7 + 4 = \boxed{}$

▶ There are _____ toys in all.

Example 2

How many apples does Eva have?

Ann's apples		Joe's apples		Eva's apples		apples in all
4	+	2	+	▇	=	9

1 Put Ann's and Joe's apples together.

4 + 2 = 6

2 Then find how many apples Eva has.

Ann's and Joe's apples		Eva's apples		apples in all
6	+	3	=	9

▶ Eva has _____ apples.

Example 3

How many blocks does Avery have?

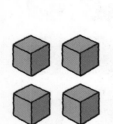 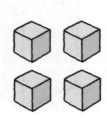 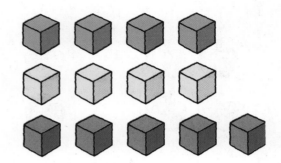

| Kevin's blocks | Avery's blocks | Ian's blocks | blocks in all |

$$4 \quad + \quad \boxed{} \quad + \quad 4 \quad = \quad 13$$

1 Put Kevin's and Ian's blocks together.

$4 + 4 = 8$

2 Then find how many blocks Avery has.

Kevin's and Ian's blocks   Avery's blocks   blocks in all

$$8 \quad + \quad \boxed{} \quad = \quad 13$$

▶ Avery has _____ blocks.

How many marbles does Chuck have?

Chuck's marbles	Kate's marbles	Mia's marbles	marbles in all

 + 5 + 3 = 14

1 Put Kate's and Mia's marbles together.

5 + _____ = _____

2 Then find how many marbles Chuck has.

Chuck's marbles	Kate's and Mia's marbles	marbles in all
	+ _____	= _____

▶ Chuck has _____ marbles.

1 How many gold stars are there in all?

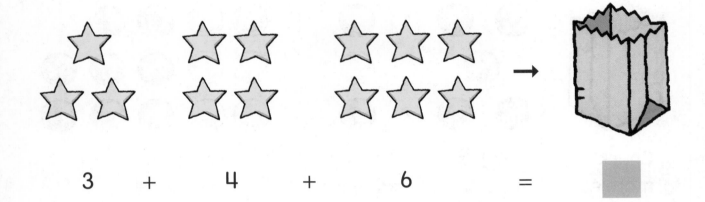

3   +   4   +   6   =

There are _____ gold stars in all.

2 How many paper clips are in the bag?

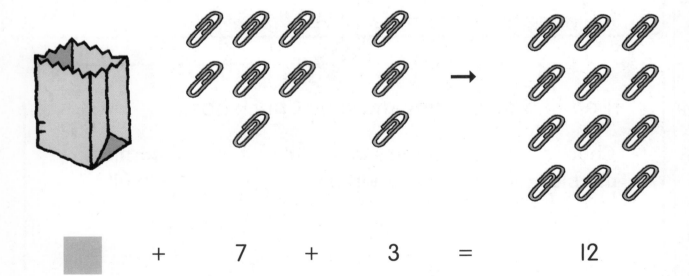

_____   +   7   +   3   =   12

There are _____ paper clips in the bag.

3 How many stickers are in the bag?

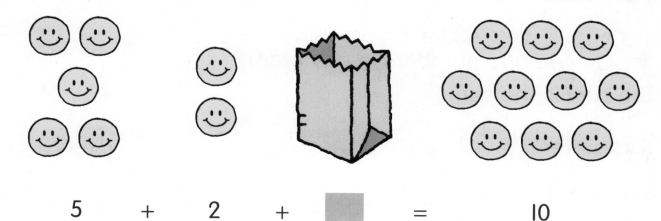

5   +   2   +   ⬜   =   10

There are _____ stickers in the bag.

4 **DRAW** There are 2 blue balloons, some red balloons, and 4 yellow balloons at a party. There are 11 balloons in all. How many red balloons are there?

2 + ⬜ + 4 = 11

There are _____ red balloons.

★ You can add numbers in any order.
The **sum** is the same.

Example 1

$5 + 2 = 7$

$2 + 5 = $ ▨

These models show the sum of 5 + 2.

5   +   2   =   7

These models show the sum of 2 + 5.

2   +   5   =   7

The sums are the same.

▶ $2 + 5 = $ ☐

The numbers being added are the same.
The order does not matter.

★ You can add three numbers.

Example 2

$2 + 3 + 4 = $

| 2 | 3 | 4 |

①

ONE WAY

Add the first two numbers.

$2 + 3 = 5$

Then add the third number.

$5 + 4 = 9$

②

ANOTHER WAY

Add the last two numbers.

$3 + 4 = 7$

Then add the first number.

$2 + 7 = 9$

The numbers are grouped in different ways.

The sum of the three numbers is the ___same___.

▶ $2 + 3 + 4 = $ ☐

Example 3

$4 + 2 + 8 = \boxed{}$

① ONE WAY

Add the first two numbers.

$4 + 2 + 8$

$6 \quad + 8$

Then add the third number.

$6 + 8 = 14$

② ANOTHER WAY

Add the last two numbers.

$4 + 2 + 8$

$4 + \quad 10$

Adding the last two numbers makes a ten.

Then add the first number.

$4 + 10 = \underline{14}$

The numbers are grouped in different ways.

The sum of the three numbers is the same.

▶ $4 + 2 + 8 = \boxed{}$

$5 + 2 + 5 = \blacksquare$

1

Look to see if you can make a ten.

Change the order of the last two numbers.

5   +   2   +   5

5   + __5__ + __2__

2

Now you can make a ten.

Add the first two numbers.

5 + 5 + 2

_____ + 2

Then add the third number.

_____ + _____ = _____

▶ $5 + 2 + 5 = \boxed{}$

Practice

Add.

1   1 + 3 = _____

      3 + 1 = _____

2   0 + 5 = _____

      5 + 0 = _____

3   5 + 6 = 11

      6 + 5 = _____

4   7 + 3 = 10

      3 + 7 = _____

5   7 + 8 = 15

      8 + 7 = _____

6   4 + 9 = 13

      9 + 4 = _____

....

7   Add two ways.

     2 + 4 + 6 = ▮

     2 + 4 + 6

     _____ + 6

     _____

     2 + 4 + 6 = ☐

     2 + 4 + 6

     2 + _____

     _____

Show how you add.

8 $2 + 1 + 9 =$ _____

9 $8 + 2 + 3 =$ _____

10 $3 + 7 + 4 =$ _____

11 $4 + 4 + 6 =$ _____

12 $3 + 5 + 5 =$ _____

13 $4 + 1 + 3 =$ _____

14 **SHOW** $4 + 5 + 5 =$ ▢

Show two ways to find the sum.

ONE WAY   ANOTHER WAY

$4 + 5 + 5 =$ ▢

How did you add the numbers?

Talk about it.

Relating Addition and Subtraction

★ Every subtraction fact has a related addition fact. **Related facts** use the same numbers.

Start with 7. Take 4 away. There are 3 left.

$7 - 4 = 3$

Start with 3. Add 4. There are 7 in all.

$3 + 4 = 7$

$7 - 4 = 3$ and $3 + 4 = 7$ are related facts.

Example

$11 - 4 = \blacksquare$

1

The numbers that you add are **addends**.

Find an addition fact that has a sum of 11 and 4 as an addend.

Think: $\blacksquare + 4 = 11$ → $\mathbf{7} + 4 = 11$

2

Use the other addend as the missing number in the subtraction fact.

$11 - 4 = \underline{7}$

 $11 - 4 = \underline{}$.

Subtract: 14 − 8 =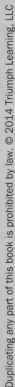

First find a related addition fact.

Use the two numbers given in the subtraction.

Which number should you use as the sum? _____14_____

Which number should you use as the addend? _____

Write the related addition fact.

_____ + _____ = _____

Which addend was not given in the subtraction? _____

Use the related addition fact to subtract.

▶ 14 − 8 = ☐

Practice

Write an addition fact that can help you subtract.

Then subtract.

1 $11 - 2 = $ ▇

_____ $+ 2 = 11$

$11 - 2 = $ ☐

2 $15 - 7 = $ ▇

_____ $+ 7 = 15$

$15 - 7 = $ ☐

3 $13 - 8 = $ ▇

_____ $+ 8 = 13$

$13 - 8 = $ ☐

4 $16 - 7 = $ ▇

_____ $+ 7 = 16$

$16 - 7 = $ ☐

Subtract.

5 $9 - 5 = $ ☐

6 $11 - 3 = $ ☐

7 $10 - 7 = $ ☐

8 $11 - 9 = $ ☐

9 $12 - 7 = $ ☐

10 $9 - 8 = $ ☐

11 13 − 5 = ☐

12 15 − 8 = ☐

13 14 − 7 = ☐

14 17 − 8 = ☐

15 16 − 9 = ☐

16 14 − 5 = ☐

17 12 − 4 = ☐

18 18 − 9 = ☐

19 **SHOW** Write 2 addition facts and 2 subtraction facts that are all related.

_____ + _____ = _____   _____ − _____ = _____

_____ + _____ = _____   _____ − _____ = _____

How do you know they are related?

Talk about it.

★ You can **count on** to add.

Example 1

6 + 2 =

1

Count on to add.

Start with the greater number.

Start with 6.

2

Count on 2.

6 → 7 _8_

▶ 6 + 2 = [ ]

Example 2

3
+ 6
___

1

Use cubes.

Start with the greater number.

Start with 6.

2

Add 3 more.

Count on 3.

6 → 7 8 $\overset{\text{9}}{\underline{}}$

▶ 3
+ 6
___
☐

Example 3

$11 - 9 = $

1 Write a related addition sentence.

9 plus what number equals 11?

$9 + $ ■ $= 11$

2 Find the missing addend.

Start with 9 cubes.

3 Count more cubes to make 11.

9   10   11

$9 + \underline{\quad 2 \quad} = 11$

▶ $11 - 9 = $ ☐

How many stars in all?

Add.

2 + 8 = ▢

1 Start with the greater number.

_____8_____ is greater than _____2_____

2 Count on to add.

Start with _____. Count on _____.

_____ ____ ____

2 + 8 = ▢

▶ There are _____ stars in all.

1 3 + 2 =

3 → _____ _____

3 + 2 = ☐

2 6 + 1 =

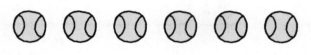

6 →   _____

6 + 1 = ☐

3 4 + 3 =

4 → _____ _____ _____

4 + 3 = ☐

4 $8 - 5 = \blacksquare$

$5 + \blacksquare = 8$

$8 - 5 = \boxed{}$

---

5 $9 - 7 = \blacksquare$

$7 + \blacksquare = 9$

$9 - 7 = \boxed{}$

6 SHOW $5 + 2 = \blacksquare$

Draw a picture.
Show how you count on to find the answer.

$5 + 2 = \boxed{}$

★ Add numbers to find the sum.

The numbers you add are addends.

One way to add is to count on.

Example 1

3 + 5 =

1 Count on to add.

Start with the greater number.

Start with 5.

2 Count on 3.

5 → 6 7 ___

▶ 3 + 5 = ☐

★ Use **doubles** and **doubles plus I** to add.

Example 2

$3 + 4 =$

①

Think about doubles.

$$3 \quad + \quad 3 \quad = \quad 6$$

②

Think about doubles plus I.

3 + 4 is I more than 3 + 3.

3 + 4 is 3 + 3 + I.

$$3 \quad + \quad 4 \quad = \quad \underline{7}$$

▶ $3 + 4 =$ ☐

Example 3

2 + 8 =

1 Write a related addition sentence.

8 + 2 =

2 Count on to add.

8 → 9, _____

▶ 2 + 8 = ☐

Example 4

7 − 6 =

1 Write a related addition sentence.

6 + = 7

2 Find the missing addend.

6   +   _____   =   7

▶ 7 − 6 = ☐

$10 - 4 = \blacksquare$

1

Show 10.

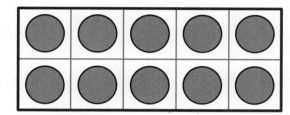

2

Subtract ___4___.

Cross out _____ counters.

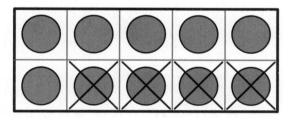

3

Count how many are left.

There are _____ counters left.

▶ $10 - 4 = \boxed{}$

Add.

1   3
    + 3

2   7
    + 2

3   2
    + 8

4   1
    + 2

5   4
    + 3

6   6
    + 1

7   5
    + 4

8   0
    + 3

9 $6 + 1 =$ _____

10 $2 + 3 =$ _____

11 $4 + 2 =$ _____

12 $9 + 0 =$ _____

13 Which facts have a sum of 10? Circle them.

$1 + 9$

$2 + 8$

$4 + 5$

$6 + 3$

$7 + 3$

$5 + 2$

$0 + 10$

$2 + 3$

$6 + 4$

$9 + 1$

$3 + 5$

$5 + 5$

Subtract.

14   3
      − 3
      ———

15   2
      − 1
      ———

16   7
      − 5
      ———

17   8
      − 4
      ———

18   10
      − 5
      ———

19   9
      − 6
      ———

20   7
      − 7
      ———

21   8
      − 6
      ———

22 $4 - 3 =$ _____

23 $5 - 2 =$ _____

24 $8 - 0 =$ _____

25 $10 - 9 =$ _____

26 Which facts have 5 as an answer? Circle them.

$8 - 3$ $5 - 5$ $7 - 4$

$9 - 3$ $5 - 0$

$6 - 5$

$8 - 2$

$4 - 1$ $7 - 2$ $6 - 1$

$10 - 5$ $9 - 4$

27 $2 + 0 =$

0

2

3

⬭

⬭

⬭

28 $9 - 0 =$

0

I

9

⬭

⬭

⬭

29 $8 - 8 =$

0

I

8

⬭

⬭

⬭

30 **WRITE** What related addition fact would you use to find $8 - 5$?

_____ + _____ = _____

How will the related fact help you?

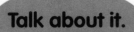 Talk about it.

★ You can count on to find a sum.

Example 1

$3 + 9 = $ ▨

1 Count on to add.

9 is greater than 3.

Start with 9.

2 Count on 3.

9 → 10 11 $\underline{12}$

The sum is 12.

▶ $3 + 9 = $ ☐

Example 2

$8 + 5 = $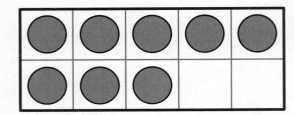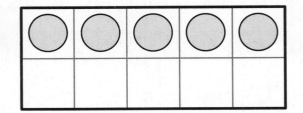

1

Make a ten. Start with 8.

Fill the **ten frame** with the yellow counters.

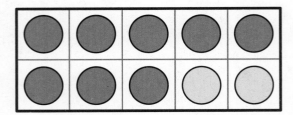 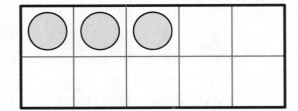

8 + 5 is the same amount as 10 + 3.

2

Count on to find the sum.

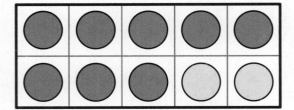 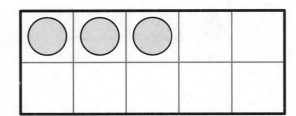

10 → 11   12   13

▶ 8 + 5 = ☐

Example 3

$15 - 7 = $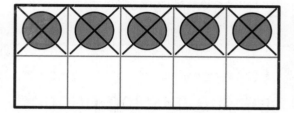

1 Show 15. Subtract to get to 10.

$15 - $ ▪ $ = 10$

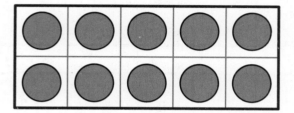

$15 - 5 = 10$

2 Break 7 into 5 and another number.

$7 = 5 + 2$

3 Subtract 2 more.

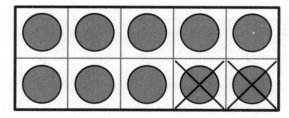 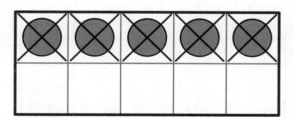

Write: $15 - 5 = 10$

$10 - 2 = \underline{\quad 8 \quad}$

▶ $15 - 7 = $ ☐

Example 4

$16 - 9 = $ ▢

1

Write a related addition sentence.

9 plus what number equals 16?

$9 + $ ▢ $ = 16$

2

Find the missing addend.

Start with 9 yellow counters.

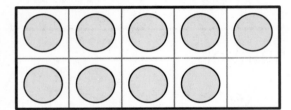

3

Use red counters to make 16.

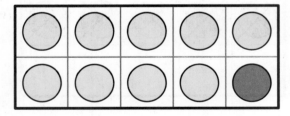 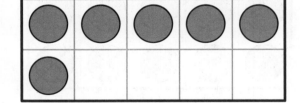

$9 + \underline{}7 = 16$

▶ $16 - 9 = $ ▢

$8 + 9 = $

1

Think about doubles.

8
+ 8
———
16

▼

2

Think about doubles plus 1.

8 + 9 is 1 more than 8 + 8.

8 + 9 is 8 + 8 + _____.

8
+ 9
———

▶ $8 + 9 = $ ☐

1   9 + 3 = ▢

9   →   ——   ——   ——

9 + 3 = ▢

2   8 + 5 = ▢

8 + 5 = ▢

3   5 + 6 = ▢

5 + 6 = ▢

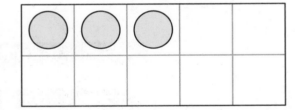

4 14 − 5 =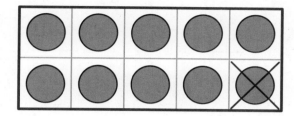

14 − 5 = ☐

....

5 17 − 9 = ☐

9 + ☐ = 17

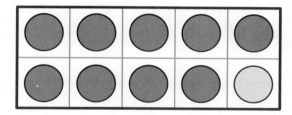

17 − 9 = ☐

....

6 16 − 8 = ☐

7   8   9

⬭   ⬭   ⬭

Add or subtract.

7   3
    + 8

8   9
    + 9

9   8
    + 7

10   6
    + 4

11   14
    − 9

12   12
    − 5

13   16
    − 7

14   13
    − 8

15 $7 + 7 =$ _____

16 $9 - 3 =$ _____

17 $5 + 9 =$ _____

18 $11 - 2 =$ _____

19 **DRAW** Make a model to show $7 + 6 =$ .

Draw counters.

Show how you found your answer.

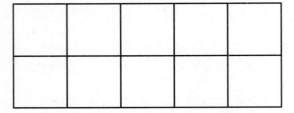 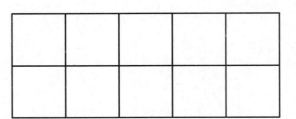

$7 + 6 =$ ☐

Lesson 9 Addition and Subtraction Equations

★ A number sentence with an **equal sign** is an **equation**.

$$\downarrow$$

$$5 + 3 = 8$$

An equation is true when both sides are equal.

Example 1

Is the equation $5 + 3 = 4 + 4$ true? Why?

$$5 + 3 = 4 + 4$$

$$\underline{}\ 8\ \underline{} = \underline{}\ 8\ \underline{}$$

▶ The equation is true because $8 = \underline{\hspace{2cm}}$.

Example 2

Is the equation true or false? Tell how you know.

$7 + 2 = 9$

1 Add: $7 + 2 = 9$

$$\underline{}\ 9\ \underline{}$$

2 Compare: $9 = 9$, so the equation is __true__.

▶ The equation is _____ because _____ = _____.

Example 3

True or false? Tell how you know.

$8 = 10 - 3$

1
> What number is equal to $10 - 3$?
>
> Think: $3 + \blacksquare = 10$
>
> $10 - 3$ is equal to 7.

2
> Compare the numbers.
>
> 8 is not equal to 7, so the equation is ___false___.

▶ The equation is _____ because _____ is not equal

to _____.

Example 4

True or false? Tell how you know.

$4 + 7 = 7 + 4$

The addends are the same on both sides.

The order does not change the sum.

The equation is ___true___.

▶ The equation is _____ because the same addends
have the same sum.

True or false? Tell how you know.

$3 + 8 = 11 - 2$

Add to find the number on the left side
of the equal sign.

$3 + \underline{} = \underline{}$

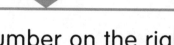

Subtract to find the number on the right side
of the equal sign.

$11 - 2 = \underline{}$

Compare. What number is equal to each side?

$3 + 8 = \underline{}$ $11 - 2 = \underline{}$

Is the equation $3 + 8 = 11 - 2$ true or false? Why?

▶ The equation is _____ because _____ is not equal

to _____.

True or false?

1 $4 = 3 + 1$ _____

2 $8 = 9 - 1$ _____

3 $9 = 9$ _____

4 $6 + 2 = 2 + 6$ _____

5 $4 + 5 = 9 + 2$ _____

6 $4 + 8 = 13 - 3$ _____

7 $9 - 3 = 7$ _____

8 $3 + 9 = 4 + 8$ _____

9 $3 + 7 = 6 + 5$ _____

10 $6 + 8 = 7 + 7$ _____

11 **FIND** What number makes the equation true?

$2 + 8 = 7 + \boxed{}$

How did you find the number?

Talk about it.

⭐ You can find a missing number in an equation.

Example 1

What is the missing number that makes the equation true?

$7 + \boxed{} = 12$

Start with 7. Count on to 12.

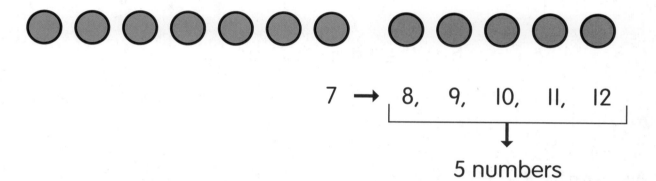

$$7 \rightarrow \underbrace{8, \quad 9, \quad 10, \quad 11, \quad 12}$$

5 numbers

$7 + \boxed{5} = 12$

▶ The missing number is _____.

★ You can use a related fact to find a missing number. Related facts use the same numbers.

Example 2

Find the missing number.

9 + ▢ = 15

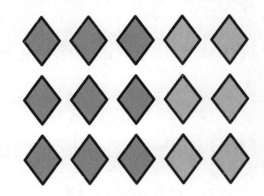

Use a related subtraction fact.

15 − 9 = [6]

The addition fact has the same numbers.

▶ 9 + [   ] = 15

Example 3

Find the missing number.

13 − ▢ = 7

Use a related addition fact.

7 + [6] = 13

The subtraction fact has the same numbers.

▶ 13 − [   ] = 7

Find the missing number.

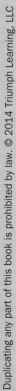 − 6 = 8

Think of a related addition fact.

Is the missing number greater than or
less than the other numbers? ___greater than___

Is the missing number the sum or an addend?

_____

Write a related addition fact.

_____ + _____ = ☐

The subtraction fact has the same numbers.

☐ − 6 = 8

▶ The missing number is _____.

Write the missing number in the box.

1 $4 + \boxed{} = 9$

$4 \longrightarrow \quad 5, \quad 6, \quad 7, \quad 8, \quad 9$

....

2 $5 + \boxed{} = 11$

3 $\boxed{} + 7 = 14$

4 $6 + 6 = \boxed{}$

5 $\boxed{} - 7 = 8$

6 $\boxed{} + 9 = 11$

7 $13 - \boxed{} = 9$

8 $11 - 3 = \boxed{}$

9 $\boxed{} - 8 = 5$

10 Which is a related subtraction fact for
$3 +$ $= 7?$

$10 - 3 = 7$ $10 - 7 = 3$ $7 - 4 = 3$

◯   ◯   ◯

....

11 Which is a related addition fact for
 $- 6 = 3?$

$9 + 3 = 12$ $3 + 6 = 9$ $6 - 3 = 3$

◯   ◯   ◯

12 **FIND** Write a related subtraction fact.
Then write the missing number.

$7 +$ ▩ $= 15$

_____ $-$ _____ $=$ _____

$7 +$ ☐ $= 15$

How did the related fact help
you find the missing number?

Talk about it.

1 Bella has 6 red blocks.

Her teacher gives her 7 blue blocks.

How many blocks does Bella have in all?

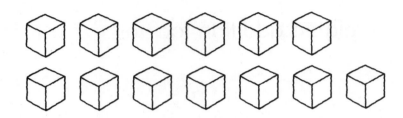

$6 + 7 =$ ☐

Bella has _____ blocks in all.

....

2 Juan had 12 pencils.

He gave some away.

He has 6 pencils left.

How many pencils did Juan give away?

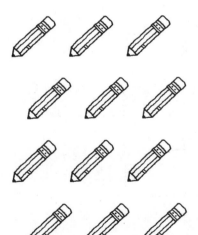

$12 -$ ☐ $= 6$

Juan gave away ____ pencils.

3 How many stickers are in the bag?

5   +   1   +      =   8

There are _____ stickers in the bag.

....

4 12 + 5 =

13   15   17

◯   ◯   ◯

....

5 8 − 4 =

5   4   2

◯   ◯   ◯

....

6 3 + 6 + 1 =

10   11   12

◯   ◯   ◯

Show how you add.

7 $3 + 7 + 2 =$ _____

8 $1 + 2 + 7 =$ _____

9 $6 + 0 + 4 =$ _____

10 $5 + 5 + 8 =$ _____

....

Write an addition fact that can help you subtract.
Then subtract.

11 $12 - 3 =$ ■

_____ $+ 3 = 12$

$12 - 3 =$ _____

12 $16 - 9 =$ ■

_____ $+ 9 = 16$

$16 - 9 =$ _____

13 $14 - 6 =$ ■

_____ $+ 6 = 14$

$14 - 6 =$ _____

14 $11 - 8 =$ ■

_____ $+ 8 = 11$

$11 - 8 =$ _____

15 $5 + 3 =$

$5 + 3 =$ ⬜

....

16 $4 + 2 =$ ▢

$4 + 2 =$ ⬜

....

17 $8 - 6 =$ ▢

$6 +$ ▢ $= 8$

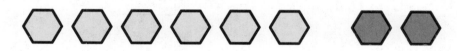

$8 - 6 =$ ⬜

18   3
     $+ 5$

19   2
     $+ 2$

20   8
     $+ 7$

21   9
     $+ 4$

22   10
     $- 5$

23   9
     $- 3$

24   16
     $- 8$

25   11
     $- 4$

26 $5 + 6 =$ _____

27 $12 - 8 =$ _____

28 $9 + 7 =$ _____

29 $8 - 6 =$ _____

Write the missing number in the box.

30 $4 + \boxed{} = 13$

31 $\boxed{} - 6 = 6$

32 **FIND** What number will make the equation below true?

$4 + 5 = 6 + \boxed{}$

How did you find the number?   **Talk about it.**

CATCH THE CONSONANTS

SCORING POINTS

B	=1	C	=2
D	=3	F	=4
G	=5	H	=6
J	=7	K	=8
L	=9	M	=10

Play a game.

Pick letters to get points. Exactly 10 points wins.

1 List ways to win with 2 letters.

_____ _____ _____ _____

1 + 9

2 List other ways to win.

_____

_____

Domain 2
Number and Operations in Base Ten

Domain 2
Number and Operations in Base Ten

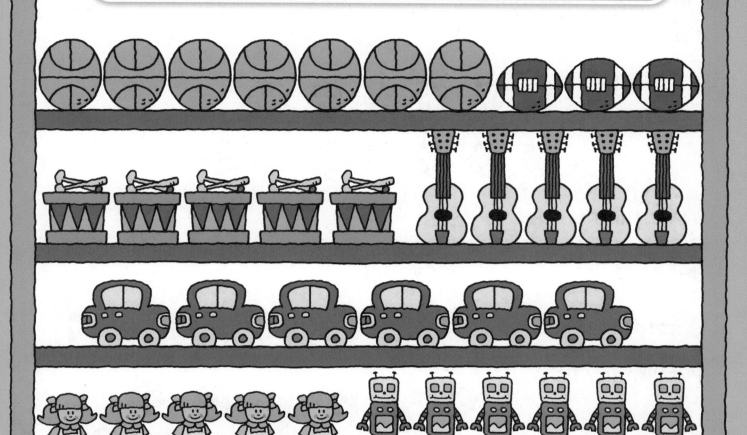

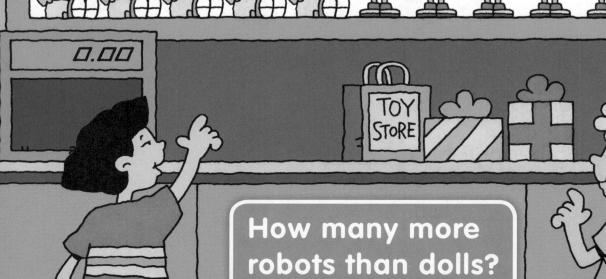

How many more robots than dolls?

Lesson 11 Counting to 120

★ You can count to find how many.

Example 1

How many ladybugs?

Count. Put a mark on each ladybug as you count.

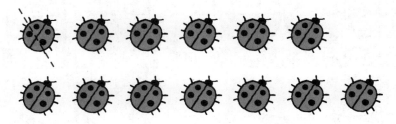

Write the number. _____13_____

▶ There are _____ ladybugs.

Example 2

How many fish?

There are fish and turtles. Count only the fish.

Put a mark on each fish as you count.

Write the number of fish. ____7____

▶ There are _____ fish.

Example 3

What number does the stand for?

What number does the stand for?

31	32	33	34	35	36	☆	38	39	40
41	42	43	44	45	46	47	48	49	50
51	52	53	♥	55	56	57	58	59	60

Start at the beginning of the row with the and count forward.

31	32	33	34	35	36	☆	38	39	40

Write the number. _____37_____

Start at the beginning of the row with the ♥ and count forward.

51	52	53	♥	55	56	57	58	59	60

Write the number. _____54_____

▶ The ☆ stands for the number _____.

The ♥ stands for the number _____.

★ You can count forward from 100.

| 101 | 102 | 103 | 104 | 105 |  | 107 | 108 | 109 | 110 |
| 111 | 112 |  | 114 | 115 | 116 | 117 | 118 | 119 | |

Example 4

What number does the ▲ stand for?

Start at the beginning of the row with the ▲.
Count forward.

Write the number that ▲ stands for. ___106___

▶ The ▲ stands for _____.

Example 5

What numbers do the ⬡ and ⬠ stand for?

Start at the beginning of the row with the ⬡ and ⬠.
Count forward.

Write the number that ⬡ stands for. ___113___

Write the number that ⬠ stands for. ___120___

▶ The ⬡ stands for _____.

The ⬠ stands for _____.

What number does each shape stand for?

41	42	43	44		46	47	48	49	50
51	52		54	55	56	57	58		60

1

Start at the beginning of the row with the △.
Count forward. Write the number in the box.

41	42	43	44	45	46	47	48	49	50

2

Start at the beginning of the row with the and the .
Count forward. Write the numbers.

51	52		54	55	56	57	58		60

The △ stands for _____.

The ⬡ stands for _____.

The ⬠ stands for _____.

1 How many ducks?

There are _____ ducks.

2 How many frogs?

15   23   32

3 Write the missing numbers to 100.

1	2		4		6	7			
11		13	14		16			19	
21		23		25	26		28	29	
	32		34				38	39	
41	42		44	45			48		50
51		53	54				58	59	
61	62	63		65		67	68		
	72		74		76	77		79	
81		83		85		87	88		90
91	92		94			97	98	99	

4 **COUNT** Start with the number 101. Count forward. Write the missing numbers.

101									
									120

How do you know you counted correctly?

Talk about it.

★ The words you say when you count are **number names**.

Count the sailboats.

| 1 | 2 | 3 | 4 | 5 | 6 | 7 |
| one | two | three | four | five | six | seven |

| 8 | 9 | 10 | 11 | 12 | 13 | 14 |
| eight | nine | ten | eleven | twelve | thirteen | fourteen |

| 15 | 16 | 17 | 18 | 19 | 20 |
| fifteen | sixteen | seventeen | eighteen | nineteen | twenty |

The last number you count is the number of sailboats.

Write and say the number of sailboats.

Write: 20

Say: twenty

Here are some more numbers and number names.

Number	Number Name
30	thirty
40	forty
50	fifty
60	sixty
70	seventy
80	eighty
90	ninety
100	one hundred
110	one hundred ten
120	one hundred twenty

Count the leaves.

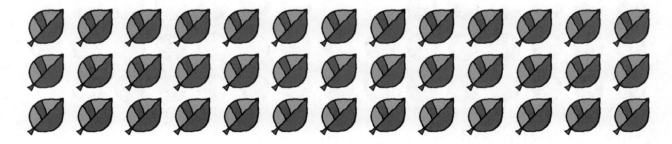

The last number you count is 39.

There are 39 leaves.

The number name for 39 is thirty-nine.

Example I

How many buttons? Count. Mark each button as you count.
Write and say the number.

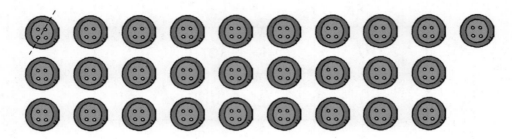

Write the last number you count. _28_

Say the number name for that number: twenty-eight

▶ There are _____ buttons.

The number name for 28 is twenty-eight.

Example 2

How many blue marbles? Mark each blue marble as you
count. Write and say the number.

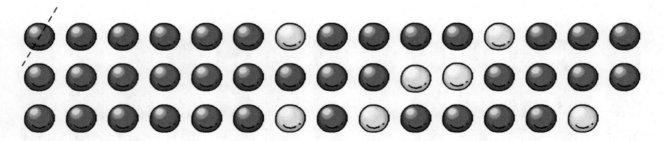

Write the last number you count. _37_

Say the number name for that number: thirty-seven

▶ There are _____ blue marbles.

The number name for 37 is thirty-seven.

How many fish?

Count the fish. Mark each fish as you count.

What is the last number you counted? __58__

Which is the number name for that number?

    forty-seven   fifty-three   fifty-eight

    ⬭   ⬭   ⬭

▶ Write the number of fish. _____

1 How many green apples?

| sixteen | twenty-one | thirty-seven |

....

2 How many ducks?

14   24   38

3 How many leaves?

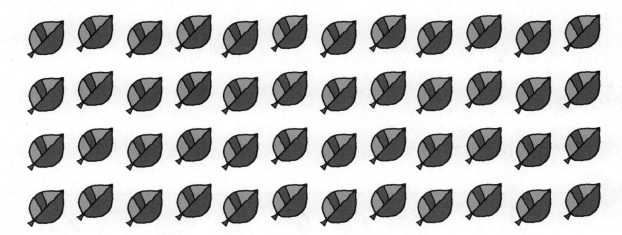

Write the number. _____

4 [DRAW] Show twenty-five flowers.

Write the number of flowers. _____

Lesson 13 Tens and Ones

★ You can show a number as **tens** and **ones**.

Example 1

How many tens and ones are in 14?

1 Show 14.

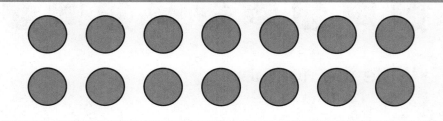

2 Make a group of 10.

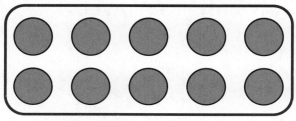

10 ones = 1 ten   4 ones

3 Write the number in the **tens and ones chart**.

Tens	Ones
1	4

▶ The number 14 has _____ ten and _____ ones.

★ You can show tens and ones as a number.

Example 2

How many counters in all?

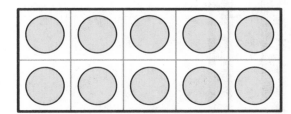 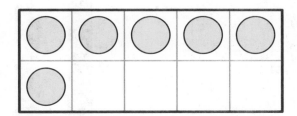

1 Look at the tens.

Look at the tens.

There is 1 ten.   1 ten = 10

2 Look at the ones.

Look at the ones.

There are 6 ones.   6 ones = 6

3 Write the number.

Write the number.

Tens	Ones
1	6

▶ There are _____ counters in all.

Example 3

How many cubes in all?

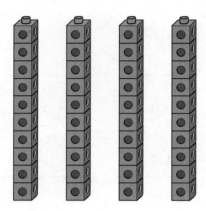

 1 Count the cubes in one stack.

There are 10 cubes in one stack.

Each stack is 10 ones or 1 ten.

2 Count the tens.

There are 4 tens.   4 tens = 40

3 Count the ones.

There are 0 ones.   0 ones = 0

4 Write the number.

▶ There are _____ cubes in all.

How many cubes in all?

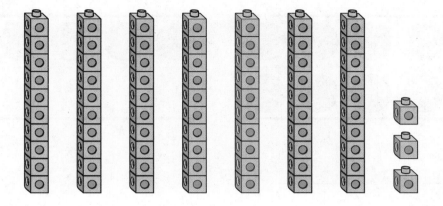

There are ___10___ cubes in each stack.

Count the tens.   _____ tens

Count the ones.   _____ ones

Write the number.

Tens	Ones

▶ There are _____ cubes in all.

1 How many tens and ones?

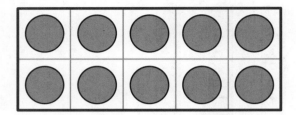 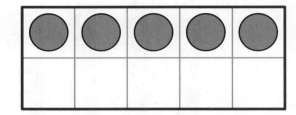

_____ ten   _____ ones

How many counters in all? _____

2 How many tens and ones?

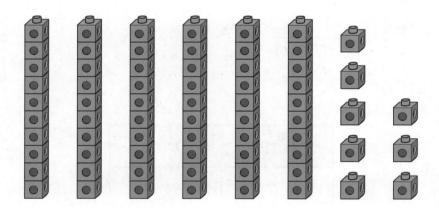

_____ tens   _____ ones

How many cubes in all? _____

3 Which number has 5 ones?

52 $\quad\quad\quad\quad$ 59 $\quad\quad\quad\quad$ 25

$\bigcirc$ $\quad\quad\quad\quad\quad$ $\bigcirc$ $\quad\quad\quad\quad\quad$ $\bigcirc$

....

4 Which number has 9 tens?

91 $\quad\quad\quad\quad$ 39 $\quad\quad\quad\quad$ 19

$\bigcirc$ $\quad\quad\quad\quad\quad$ $\bigcirc$ $\quad\quad\quad\quad\quad$ $\bigcirc$

5 **DRAW** Make groups of 10.

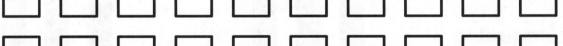
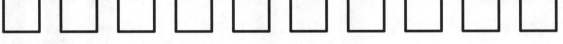
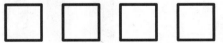

How many tens and ones?

_____ tens $\quad\quad$ _____ ones

How many in all? _____

Lesson 14 — Comparing Numbers

★ You can compare numbers.

20 is **greater than** 10.

20 > 10

20   10

31 is **equal to** 31.

31 = 31

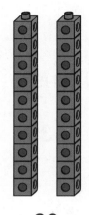 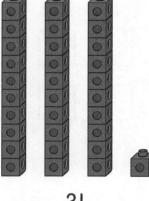 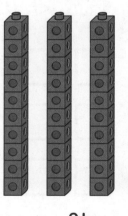

31   31

23 is **less than** 26.

23 < 26

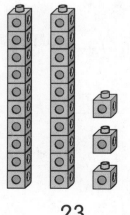 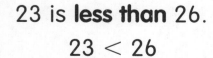 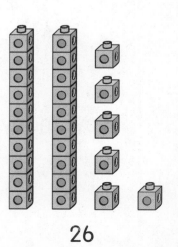

23   26

Example 1

Compare the numbers. Write >, =, or <.

24 ◯ 18

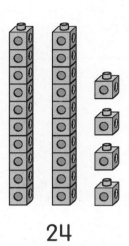   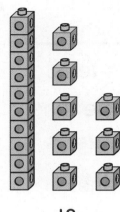

24   18

1
Look at the tens.

2̲4 has 2 tens.

1̲8 has 1 ten.

⬇

2
Compare the tens.

2 tens is greater than 1 ten.

24 is greater than 18.

⬇

3
Write >, =, or <.

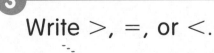 _____ means is greater than.

▶ 24 ◯ 18

Example 2

Compare the numbers. Write >, =, or <.

52 ◯ 57

1

Look at the tens.

Compare the tens.

5̲2 has 5 tens.

5̲7 has 5 tens.

The tens are the same.

2

Look at the ones.

Compare the ones.

5̲2̲ has 2 ones.

5̲7̲ has 7 ones.

2 ones is less than 7 ones.

52 is less than 57.

3

Write >, =, or <.

_____ means is less than.

▶ 52 ◯ 57

Compare the numbers. Write >, =, or <.

76 ◯ 73

1

Look at the tens.

76 has __7__ tens.

73 has ____ tens.

The tens are the same.

▼

2

Look at the ones.

76 has ____ ones.

73 has ____ ones.

▼

3

Compare the ones.

6 ones is _____ than 3 ones.

So 76 is _____ than 73.

Write >, =, or <.

▶ 76 ◯ 73

Practice

Compare. Write >, =, or <.

1   20 ◯ 30

2   30 ◯ 10

3   25 ◯ 15

4   14 ◯ 14

5   20 ◯ 25

6 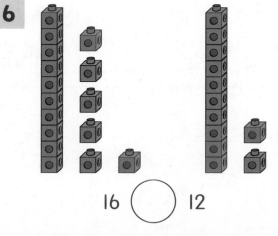 16 ◯ 12

Compare. Circle the answer.

7 Which is greater?

70   80

8 Which is greater?

61   58

9 Which is less?

75   74

10 Which is greater?

90   98

Compare. Write >, =, or <.

11 12 ◯ 23

12 27 ◯ 27

13 84 ◯ 75

14 65 ◯ 60

15 31 ◯ 32

16 76 ◯ 79

17 52 ◯ 52

18 43 ◯ 28

19 **COMPARE** Write five numbers that are greater than 20 and less than 40.

_____

Compare two of your numbers. Write >, =, or <.

_____ ◯ _____

⭐ Use models to help you add.

Example 1

12 + 6 = ■

1

Show 12 and 6.

2

Add the ones.

2 ones + 6 ones = 8 ones

3

Find the sum.

1 ten 8 ones = ___18___

▶ 12 + 6 = _____

Example 2

$26 + 8 =$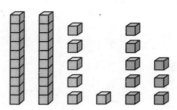

 Show 26 and 8.

2   Add the ones.

6 ones + 8 ones = 14 ones

3   Make a ten.

14 ones = 1 ten 4 ones

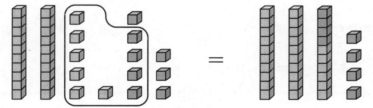

4   Find the sum.

3 tens 4 ones = _34_

▶ 26 + 8 = _____

Example 3

$45 + 20 =$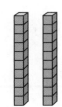

1

Show each number.

Show 45.

Show 20.

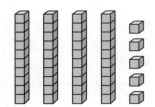

$45 = 4$ tens 5 ones

$20 = 2$ tens 0 ones

2

Add.

Add the ones.

5 ones $+ 0$ ones $= 5$ ones

Add the tens.

4 tens $+ 2$ tens $= 6$ tens

3

Find the sum.

6 tens 5 ones $= \underline{\quad 65 \quad}$

▶ $45 + 20 = \underline{\qquad}$

16 + 7 = ▮

1

Show 16 and 7.

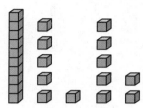

2

Add the ones.

6 ones + 7 ones = ___13___ ones

3

Make a ten.

13 ones = _____ ten _____ ones

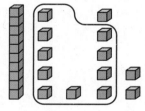

4

Find the sum.

_____ tens _____ ones = _____

▶ 16 + 7 = _____

1 14 + 6 =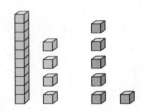

14 + 6 = _____

- -

2 57 + 5 = ▢

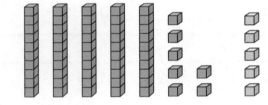

57 + 5 = _____

- -

3 29 + 40 = ▢

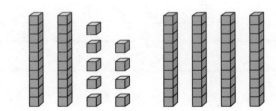

29 + 40 = _____

4 45 + 3 =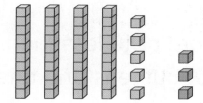

45 + 3 = _____

....

5 76 + 20 = ▢

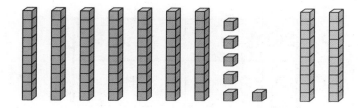

76 + 20 = _____

6 DRAW 23 + 7 = ▢

Draw models to find the sum.

23 + 7 = _____

Lesson 16 10 More or 10 Less

★ You can find 10 more or 10 less than a number.
Use what you know about tens and ones.

Example 1

What number is 10 more than 14?

1 Show 14 as tens and ones.

Tens	Ones
1	4

2 Show **1 ten more**.

Do not change the ones.

Tens	Ones
1	4

↓ ↓

Tens	Ones
2	4

▶ The number _____ is 10 more than 14.

Example 2

What number is 10 less than 26?

Show 26 as tens and ones.

Tens	Ones
2	6

↓   ↓

Show **1 ten less**.

Tens	Ones
1	6

▶ The number _____ is 10 less than 26.

★ You can use mental math to find 10 more or 10 less than a number.

Example 3

What number is 10 more than 85?

Think: In the number 85, the 8 stands for 8 tens.

    1 ten more than 8 tens is 9 tens.

    So 10 more than 85 is 95.

▶ The number _____ is 10 more than 85.

What number is 10 less than 49?

Use mental math.

In the number 49, what does the 9 stand for? ___9___ ones

In the number 49, what does the 4 stand for? _____

To show 10 less than 49, will the 9 change
or will it stay the same?

_____

To show 10 less than 49, will the 4 change
or will it stay the same?

_____

How many tens are in 49? _____

How many tens are in the number that is 10 less than 49?

_____

▶ The number _____ is 10 less than 49.

Practice

1 What number is 10 more than 25?

Tens	Ones
2	5

↓ ↓

Tens	Ones

The number _____ is 10 more than 25.

....

2 What number is 10 less than 42?

Tens	Ones
4	2

↓ ↓

Tens	Ones

The number _____ is 10 less than 42.

3 What number is 10 less than 51? _____

4 What number is 10 more than 39? _____

5 What number is 10 more than 72? _____

6 What number is 10 less than 19? _____

7 What number is 10 more than 84? _____

8 What number is 10 less than 93? _____

9 What number is 10 more than 66? _____

10 **NAME** The number 58 is 10 more than what number? _____

How do you know?

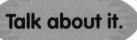
Talk about it.

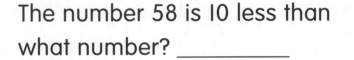

The number 58 is 10 less than what number? _____

How do you know?

Talk about it.

Lesson 17 Subtracting Tens

★ Use models to help you subtract.

Example 1

$30 - 20 =$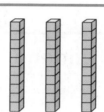

1 Show 30.

30 = 3 tens

2 Subtract 20.

20 = 2 tens, so subtract 2 tens.

3 tens − 2 tens = 1 ten

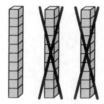

3 Find the answer.

1 ten = _____10_____

▶ 30 − 20 = _____

Example 2

$80 - 50 = \blacksquare$

Write a related addition sentence.

50 plus what number equals 80?

$50 + \blacksquare = 80$

2
Find the missing addend. Use models.

Start with 50.

50 = 5 tens

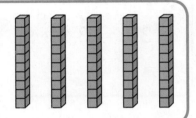

3
Add tens to make 80.   80 = 8 tens

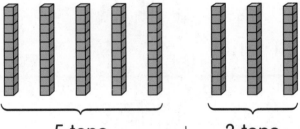

5 tens   +   3 tens   = 8 tens

4
Find the answer.

The missing addend is 3 tens.

3 tens = ___30___

▶ $80 - 50 = $ _____

70 − 30 =

1

Show 70.

70 = ___7___ tens

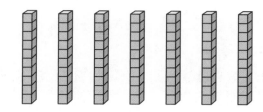

2

Subtract 30.

30 = _____ tens

Subtract _____ tens

7 tens − 3 tens = _____ tens

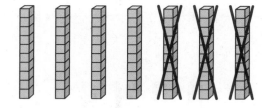

Find the answer.

4 tens = _____

▶ 70 − 30 = _____

1 60 − 40 = ◻

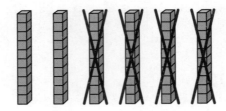

60 − 40 = _____

2 50 − 10 = ◻

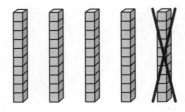

50 − 10 = _____

3 40 − 20 = ◻

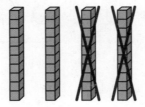

40 − 20 = _____

4 90 − 30 =

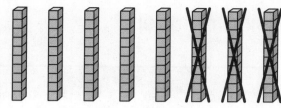

90 − 30 = _____

....

5 70 − 60 =

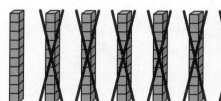

70 − 60 = _____

6 **DRAW** 80 − 20 =

Draw models to find the answer.

80 − 20 = _____

1 Write the missing numbers.

1	2	3		5	6		8		10
11			14		16			19	
	22	23		25					
31	32		34				38	39	
		43	44	45					50
51	52				56		58		60
61		63		65		67		69	
	72		74		76			79	
81		83		85		87	88		90
	92		94				98	99	
101	102	103		105			108		110
111	112			115		117		119	

....

2 Start with the number 102. Count forward. Write the next 10 numbers.

102, _____, _____, _____, _____, _____,

_____, _____, _____, _____, _____

3 How many stickers?

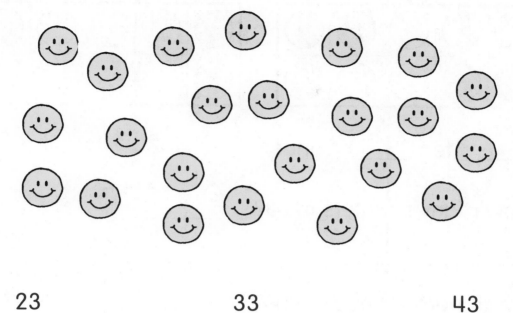

23   33   43
⬭   ⬭   ⬭

....

4 What is the number name for 35?

twenty-five   thirty-five   forty-five
⬭   ⬭   ⬭

....

5 Make a group of 10. Ring it.

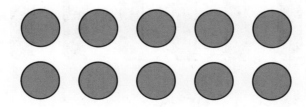

10 ones = _____ ten

6 How many tens and ones?

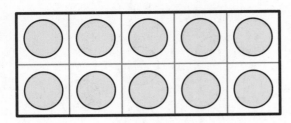 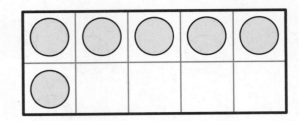

_____ ten _____ ones

How many counters in all? _____

···

7 Which number has 7 tens?

57   17   72

$\bigcirc$ $\bigcirc$ $\bigcirc$

···

8 How many tens and ones?

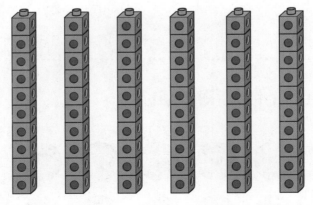

_____ tens _____ ones

How many cubes in all? _____

Compare. Write >, =, or <.

9
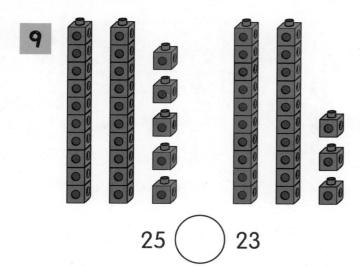

25 ◯ 23

---

10 14 ◯ 14

11 36 ◯ 41

12 NAME The number 46 is 10 more than what number? _____

How do you know?

Talk about it.

The number 46 is 10 less than what number? _____

How do you know?

Talk about it.

Add.

13   15 + 7 =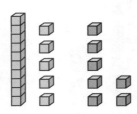

15 + 7 = _____

....

14   55 + 20 = ▢

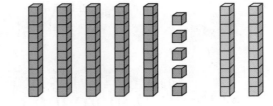

55 + 20 = _____

15   **SHOW** Use the models to subtract. 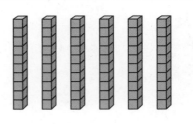

60 − 20 = ▢

60 − 20 = _____

How did you find your answer?

Talk about it.

Who is the Winner?

Two boys had a hopping contest.

The winner is the boy with the most hops.

First they hopped on their right foot.

Who was the winner?

Read the clues.

Right-Foot Winner

 José had 24 jumps on his right foot.

 Nick had 24 + 20 jumps on his right foot.

 Nick had _____ jumps on his right foot.

The winner is _____. **Talk about it**

Next they each hopped on their left foot.

Who was the winner?

Left-Foot Winner

 José had 34 jumps on his left foot.

 Nick had 10 fewer jumps on his left foot than José.

Nick had _____ jumps on his left foot.

The winner is _____. **Talk about it.**

Domain 3
Measurement and Data

Domain 3
Measurement and Data

Which leaf is longer?

★ You can compare **lengths**.

Line up the objects on one side.

Example 1

Which is shorter?

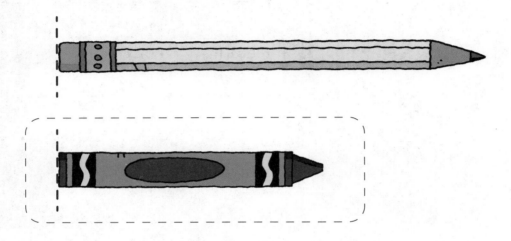

▶ The crayon is _____ than the pencil.

Example 2

Which is longer?

▶ The comb is _____ than the paper clip.

Example 3

Order the objects from longest to shortest.

1. Line up the objects.

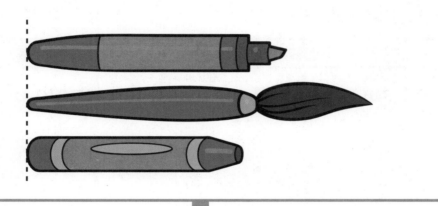

2. Compare.

The paintbrush goes across the farthest so it is the longest.

The end of the crayon is closest to the start so it is the

_____shortest_____.

▶ The order from longest to shortest is _____ ,

_____ , _____ .

Example 4

Which baseball bat is longer?

baseball bat A

baseball bat B

1

Use a stick to measure the length of baseball bat A.

Baseball bat A is ___shorter___ than the stick.

2

Use the same stick to measure the length of baseball bat B.

Baseball bat B is _____ than the stick.

▶ So baseball bat B is _____ than baseball bat A.

Which fishing rod is shorter?

fishing rod A   fishing rod B

1

Use a stick to measure the length of fishing rod A.

_____

Fishing rod A is __longer__ than the stick.

2

Use the same stick to measure fishing rod B.

_____

Fishing rod B is _____ than the stick.

▶ Fishing rod B is _____ than fishing rod A.

1 Which is longer, the feather or the spoon?

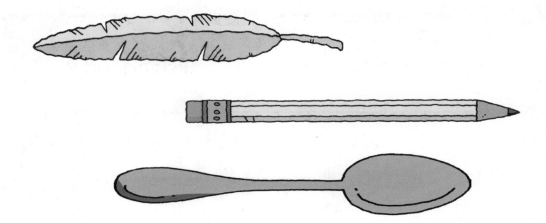

Use the pencil to compare.

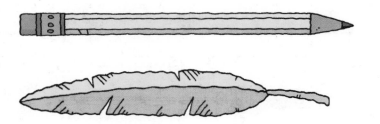

The pencil is _____ than the feather.

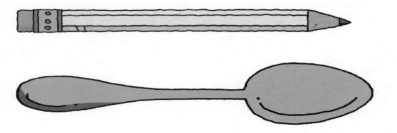

The spoon is _____ than the pencil.

The spoon is _____ than the feather.

2 Order the lines from shortest to longest.

_____

_____

_____

_____ _____ _____

3 **DRAW** Look at the pencil.

Draw a shorter pencil above the pencil.

Draw a longer pencil below the pencil.

Are they in order from shortest to longest? _____

Talk about it.

★ You can measure the length of objects.

Choose an object to use as the **unit** for measuring.

Line up the units end to end.

Example

How long is the pencil?

Use cubes as the unit of measure.

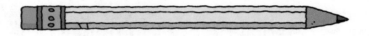

1 Start at one end of the pencil.

Connect cubes to match the length of the pencil.

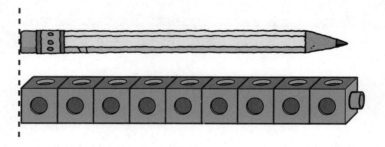

2 Count the cubes. _____ cubes

▶ The pencil is _____ cubes long.

How long is the paintbrush? Use paper clips as the unit of measure.

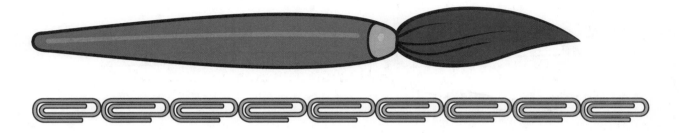

1

Look at both ends of the paintbrush.

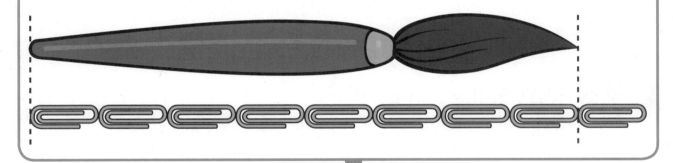

2

Count the paper clips between the ends.

There are _____ paper clips.

▶ The paintbrush is _____ paper clips long.

1 How long are the scissors?

Use paper clips to measure.

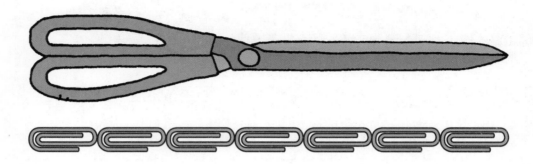

The scissors are _____ paper clips long.

· ·

2 How long is the comb?

Use cubes to measure.

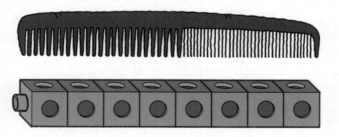

The comb is _____ cubes long.

3 **DECIDE** Luke used paper clips to measure the feather.

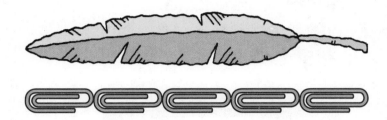

Chung used paper clips to measure the feather.

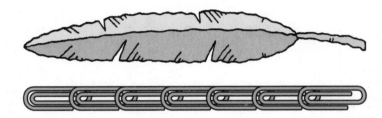

Kayla used paper clips to measure the feather.

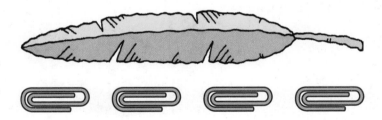

Who measured correctly? _____

How do you know?

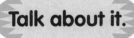

Talk about it.

How long is the feather?

_____ paper clips long

★ You can use **clocks** to tell **time**.

This clock shows eight o'clock.

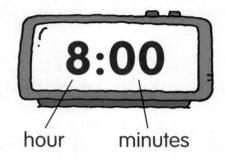

hour   minutes

This clock also shows eight o'clock.

minute hand

hour hand

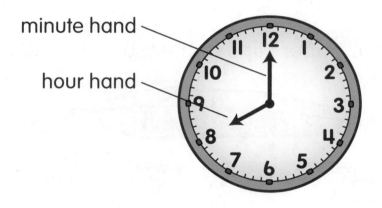

The **hour hand** points to the **hour**.

The **minute hand** tells how many **minutes** have passed.

Write: 8:00

Say: eight o'clock

Example 1

What time does the clock show?

1 The hour hand is the shorter hand.

Look at where it points to find the hour.

It points to the 3.

2 The minute hand is the longer hand.

When it points to 12, say o'clock.

3 Write the time.

First write the hour and then the minutes.

3 : 00
_____:_____

Say the time.   three o'clock

▶ The time is _____:_____.

★ There are 60 minutes in 1 hour.

Half of 60 minutes is 30 minutes.

So there are 30 minutes in a **half hour**.

Example 2

What time does the clock show?

1 The hour hand is between 9 and 10.

It is between 9 o'clock and 10 o'clock.

It is past 9 o'clock.

2 The minute hand is halfway around the clock.

When it points to 6, say 30.

It is 30 minutes after 9 o'clock.

3 Write the time. ___9___:___30___

Say the time. nine thirty

▶ The time is _____:_____.

What time does the clock show?

1 The hour hand is between ___4___ and ___5___.

It is between _____ o'clock and _____ o'clock.

It is past _____ o'clock.

2 The minute hand is halfway around the clock.

It points to _____.

It is _____ minutes past the hour.

3 Write the time.   _____:_____.

Say the time.   _____ thirty

▶ The time is _____:_____.

1 What time does the clock show?

The hour hand points to the _____.

The minute hand points to the _____.

The time is _____:_____.

---

2 What time does the clock show?

The hour hand is

between _____ and _____.

It is past _____ o'clock.

The minute hand points to the _____.

It is _____ minutes after _____ o'clock.

The time is _____:_____.

What time does the clock show?

3

_____:_____

4

_____:_____

5

_____:_____

6

_____:_____

7

_____:_____

8

_____:_____

9 **DRAW** Look at the clock.

Write the time. _____:_____

Show the same time on this clock.
Draw the hands.

★ Use a **table** to show **data**.

Use **tally marks** to show how many.

1	2	3	4	5
● |	● ● ||	● ● ● |||	● ● ● ● ||||	● ● ● ● ● 卌

6	7	8	9	10
● ● ● ● ● ● 卌 |	● ● ● ● ● ● ● 卌 ||	● ● ● ● ● ● ● ● 卌 |||	● ● ● ● ● ● ● ● ● 卌 ||||	● ● ● ● ● ● ● ● ● ● 卌 卌

This table shows votes for favorite color.

Each \| stands for 1 vote.

Each 卌 stands for 5 votes.

Favorite Color

red	||||
yellow	卌
blue	||

There were 4 votes for red.

There were 5 votes for yellow.

There were 2 votes for blue.

Example 1

The table shows the number of marbles in a bag.

Marbles in a Bag

red	|||
green	||||
blue	ⵌ ||

How many blue marbles are in the bag?

1 Find the row for blue marbles.

blue	ⵌ ||

2 Count the tally marks for blue.

Each | stands for 1 marble.

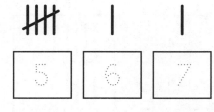

▶ There are _____ blue marbles in the bag.

Example 2

How many marbles are in the bag?

Marbles in a Bag

red	|||
green	||||
blue	ⵊ ||

1

Find the row for red marbles.

There are 3 red marbles.

2

Find the row for green marbles.

There are 4 green marbles.

3

Find the row for blue marbles.

There are 7 blue marbles.

4

Add the numbers.

3 + 4 + 7 = _____14_____

▶ There are _____ marbles in the bag.

Example 3

Lauren has these pieces of fruit.

Show the data in a table.

1 Count the number of each kind of fruit.

5 apples

3 bananas

7 oranges

2 Use tally marks to show the different kinds of fruit.

Each | stands for 1 piece of fruit.

Lauren's Fruits

apples	bananas	oranges
⅃⅃⅃⅂		

 **Try**

This table shows the kinds of flowers in the garden.

Flowers in the Garden

rose	~~IIII~~ IIII
daisy	II
tulip	~~IIII~~ II

How many more roses than tulips?

1

Find the row for roses.

There are _____9_____ roses.

2

Find the row for tulips.

There are _____ tulips.

3

Subtract to find how many more.

_____ − _____ = _____

▶ There are _____ more roses than tulips.

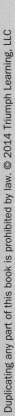

The table shows the number of animals in the zoo.

Animals in the Zoo

lion	||||
tiger	卌
monkey	卌 |||

1 How many lions? _____

2 How many tigers? _____

3 How many monkeys? _____

4 How many more tigers than lions?

_____

5 How many fewer tigers than monkeys?

_____

6 How many animals are in the zoo in all?

_____

ORGANIZE David asked some children to show their favorite drinks.

7 Show the data in the table.
Count how many of each drink.

_____ milk   _____ juice   _____ water

Write a title for your table.
Draw a tally mark for each drink shown.

Title _____

milk	juice	water

8 How many more children like water than juice?

_____

9 How many children did David ask in all? _____

Domain 3 Review

1 Order the objects from shortest to longest.

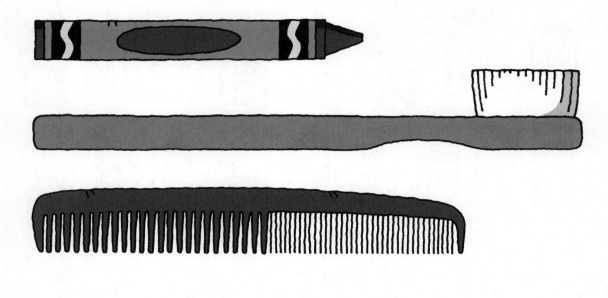

_____, _____, _____

2 Order the lines from shortest to longest.

_____, _____, _____

3 Is guitar A longer or shorter than guitar B?

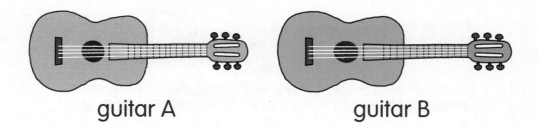

guitar A   guitar B

Use a stick to compare.

Guitar A is _____ than the stick.

Use the same stick to measure guitar B.

Guitar B is _____ than the stick.

So guitar A is _____ than guitar B.

4 How long is the fork?

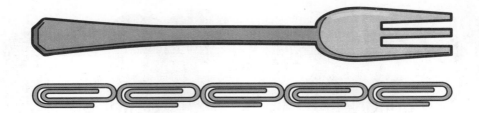

5 paper clips   6 paper clips   7 paper clips

5 How long is the paintbrush?

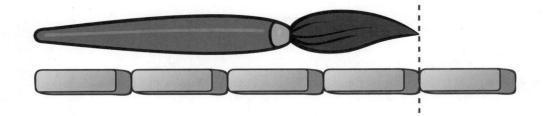

3 erasers   4 erasers   5 erasers

What time does the clock show?

6

_____:_____

7

_____:_____

8 Look at the clock.

Write the time. _____:_____

Show the same time on this clock.
Draw the hands.

The table shows the kinds of fish in the class aquarium.

Fish in the Aquarium

clownfish	llll
guppy	⊬⊬ ll
goldfish	⊬⊬

9 How many clownfish? _____

10 How many guppies? _____

11 How many goldfish? _____

12 How many more guppies than goldfish?

_____

13 How many fish are in the aquarium in all?

_____

14 DRAW The class also has angel fish. There are more angel fish than goldfish. There are fewer angel fish than guppies. Draw tally marks to show the number of angel fish.

COMPARE THE RIBBONS

Use paper clips. Measure each ribbon.

1

The blue ribbon is _____ paper clips long.

2

The red ribbon is _____ paper clips long.

3

The green ribbon is _____ paper clips long.

4 Order the ribbons from longest to shortest.

_____ _____ _____

5 How do the paper clips help you order
the ribbons?

Talk about it.

Domain 4
Geometry

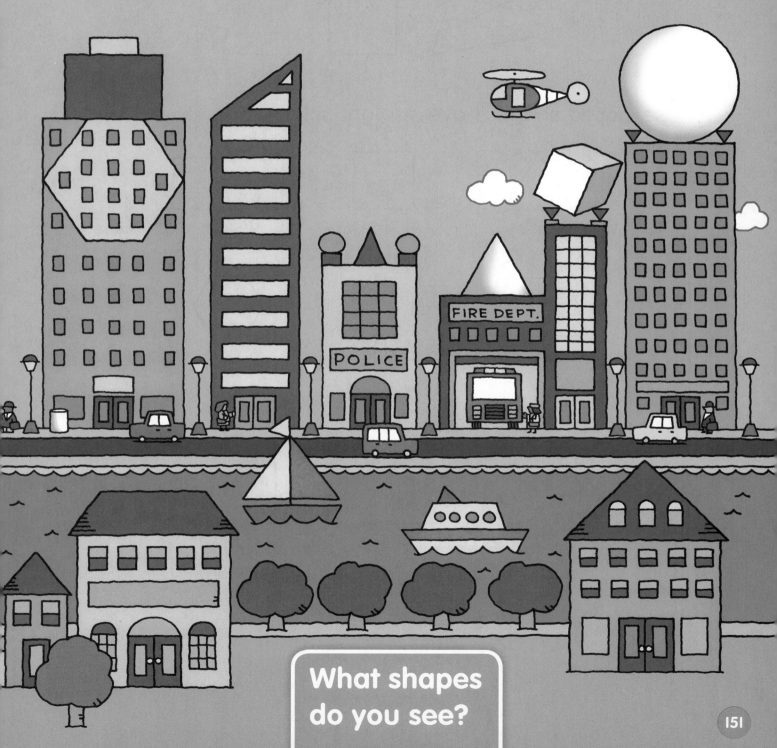

Geometry

What shapes do you see?

★ There are many different kinds of shapes.

These shapes are **open shapes**.

These **closed shapes** have straight **sides**.

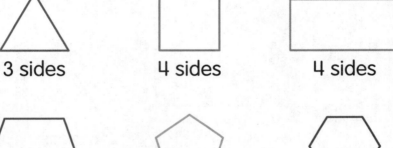

| 3 sides | 4 sides | 4 sides |

| 4 sides | 5 sides | 6 sides |

These closed shapes have curves.

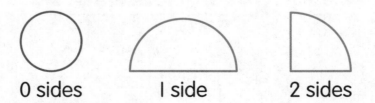

| 0 sides | 1 side | 2 sides |

Example I

Tell what you know about
this triangle.

 corner

side

Which things are true for *all* triangles?

This triangle is green and large.
One of its corners points straight up.
It is closed.
It has 3 sides and 3 corners.

A triangle can be any color.

A triangle can be any size.

The corners of a triangle can
point in any direction.

All triangles are closed.

All triangles have ___3___ sides and ___3___ corners.

▶ All triangles are closed and have _____ sides and
_____ corners.

Example 2

Tell what you know about this square.

Which things are true for *all* squares?

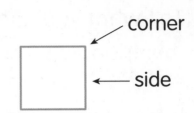

corner

side

This square is blue and small.
One of its sides is at the top.
The square is closed.
All the sides are the same length.
It has 4 sides and 4 corners.

A square can be any color.

A square can be any size.

A square can be turned
in any direction.

All squares are closed and have sides that are the
same length.

All squares have _____ sides and _____ corners.

▶ All squares are closed.
  All squares have sides that are the same length.

  All squares have _____ sides and _____ corners.

Which shape is a triangle?

A 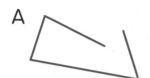 B   C   D

1

Shape *A* is open. Is shape *A* a triangle? _____

2

Shape *B* has _____ sides and _____ corners.

Is shape *B* a triangle? _____

3

Shape *C* has a curved side. Is it a triangle? _____

4

Shape *D* has _____ sides and _____ corners.

Is shape D a triangle? _____

▶ Shape _____ is a triangle.

A triangle is   open   closed. (Ring the answer.)

Its sides are   straight   curved. (Ring the answer.)

It has _____ sides and _____ corners.

1 Which is true of all these shapes?

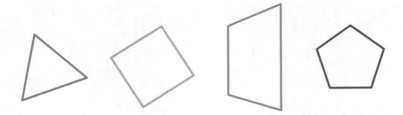

◯ All the shapes have 4 sides.

◯ All the shapes have curved sides.

◯ All the shapes have more than 2 corners.

---

2 This shape is a square.

Which is true about all squares?

◯ All squares are green.

◯ All squares have 4 corners.

◯ All squares have a side that faces straight up.

3 Which is NOT true about all triangles?

◯ All triangles have 3 sides and 3 corners.

◯ All triangles are the same size and color.

◯ All triangles are closed and have straight sides.

4 Draw a square.

5 Draw a triangle.

6 **COMPARE** How are a square and a triangle alike? How are a square and a triangle different?

Talk about it.

7 **USE** This shape is a rectangle.

Use real objects. Put your objects together to make a larger rectangle.

You can use straws like this.

★ You already know that a **flat shape** can have straight sides, corners, curves, or all of these.

A block, a box, a can, or a cone is a **solid shape**.
The solid shapes below have **faces**.
A face is a flat shape that is part of a solid shape.

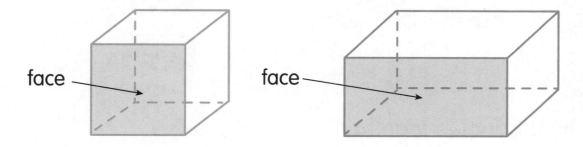

This solid shape is curved. It has no faces.

These solid shapes are curved and also have faces.

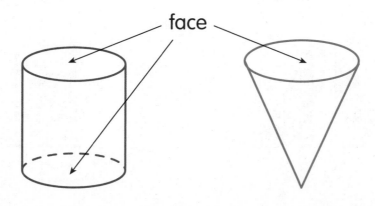

★ You can put flat shapes together to make a new flat shape.

Put two squares together to make a rectangle.

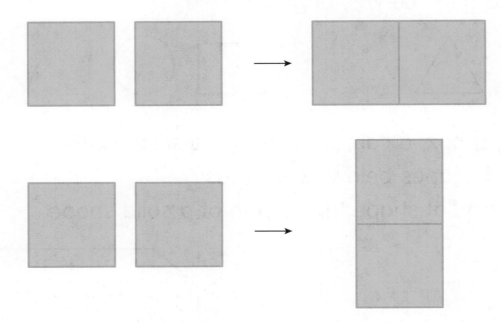

Put two triangles together.

You can make a new triangle or a rectangle.

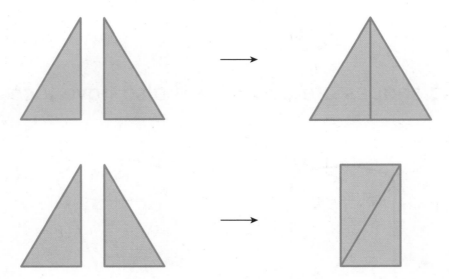

★ You can make new shapes by putting shapes together.

Molly made this shape using a square and triangles.

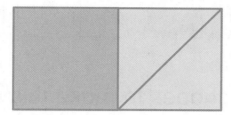

Example 1

What is another shape you can make using a square and triangles?

Use one square and two triangles.

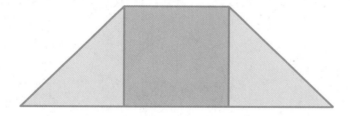

▶ You can make a ___trapezoid___.

Example 2

What shape can you make using only triangles?

Use four triangles.

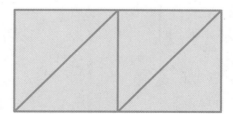

▶ You can make a _____.

Example 3

Zaid has these shapes.

He used two of the shapes to make this circle.

He used three of the shapes to make this circle.

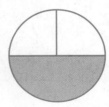

How many of the shapes did he use to make this circle?

▶ Zaid used _____ of the shapes.

★ You can put solid shapes together to make a new solid shape.

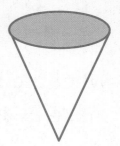
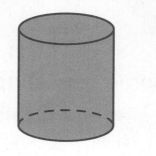

When you put solid shapes together, look for faces that are the same size and shape.

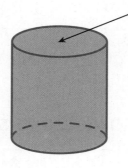
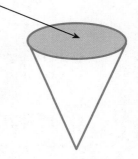

The curved faces look like they are the same size and shape. Turn the shapes to see if the curved faces match.

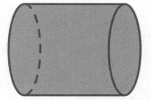
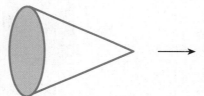
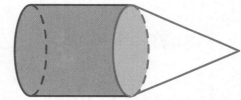

Here is the new shape.

What are some new shapes you can make by taking apart this solid shape?

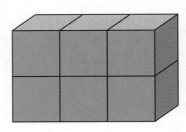

1

Each 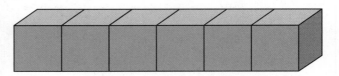 is 1 cube. How many cubes

are there in the large solid shape above? _____ 6

2

Take apart the large solid shape to make some new solid shapes.

How many new shapes like this

can you make? _____

How many new shapes like this

can you make? _____

3

Which of these new shapes can you make using all 6 cubes? Circle it.

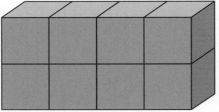

1 This flat shape is a hexagon.

Which group of shapes below can you put together to make this hexagon?

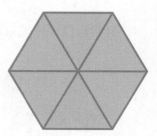

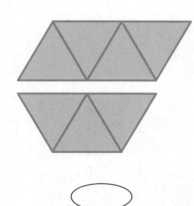 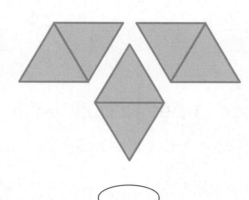 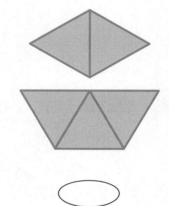

2 Which shape below can you make with this group of shapes?

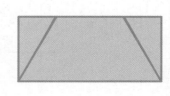

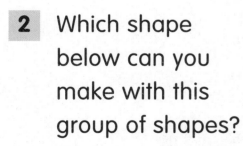 

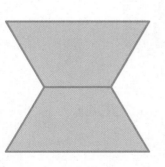 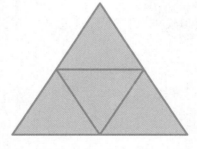

3 Which solid shape below can you make with this group of cubes?

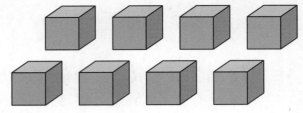

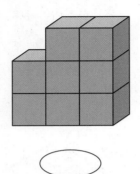 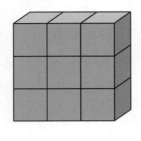 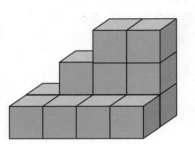

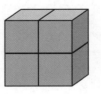

⬭ ⬭ ⬭

4 **USE** Linda used cubes to build this solid shape. How many cubes did she use? _____

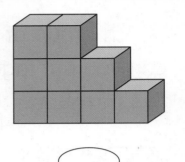

Then she used the solid shape she made to build the 2 new shapes shown below.

Tell how many cubes she used for each shape.

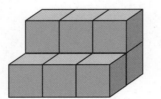 

_____ cubes   _____ cubes

Lesson 24 Making Equal Shares

★ You can make **equal shares** from any whole circle.

This is a whole circle.

Here is the same circle.
It is cut into 2 equal shares.
Each share is **half** of the whole circle.

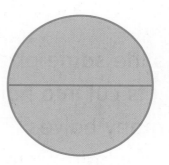

Now the circle is cut into
4 equal shares. Each share
is a **fourth** of the whole circle.
A fourth is also called a **quarter.**

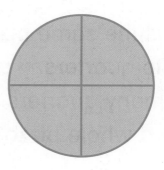

This circle is cut into 8 equal shares.
As a circle is cut into more and more
equal shares, the shares get smaller
and smaller.

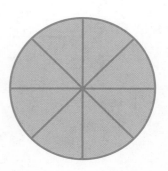

Example 1

How many halves make a whole?

How many quarters make a whole?

This is a whole pizza.

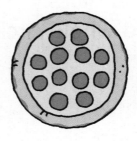

This is the same pizza.
Now it is cut into halves.
How many halves
make a whole pizza? ___2___ halves

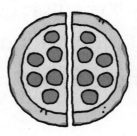

Here is the same pizza
cut into quarters.
How many quarters
make a whole pizza? ___4___ quarters

▶ There are _____ halves in a whole.

There are _____ quarters in a whole.

★ You can make equal shares from a whole rectangle.

whole   halves   fourths

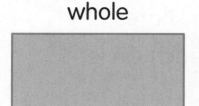 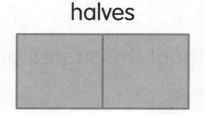 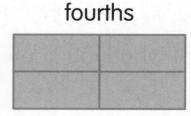

Example 2

These squares below are the same size.
Tell about each square.

square A

There are 2 equal shares.

Each share is a __half__
of the whole square.

square B

There are 4 equal shares.

Each share is a __fourth__
of the whole square.

▶ Square A has _____ equal shares.

Each share is a _____ of the whole square.

Square B has _____ equal shares.

Each share is a _____ of the whole square.

The circles below are each cut into equal shares.
Tell what you know about the shares of each circle.

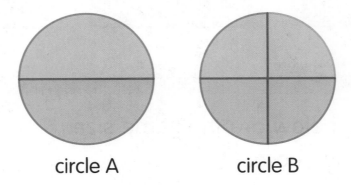

circle A   circle B

Look at the blue and red circle.

The circle is cut into how many equal shares? _____2_____

Each share is a _____ of the whole circle.

How many halves make up the whole circle?

▶ _____ halves make up the whole circle.

Look at the other circle.

The circle is cut into how many equal shares? _____

Each equal share is a _____ of the whole circle.

How many fourths make up the whole circle?

▶ _____ fourths make up the whole circle.

Use the rectangle below for questions 1 and 2.

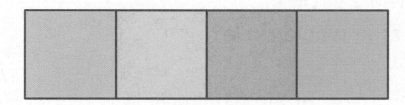

1 The rectangle is cut into how many equal shares?

2   3   4

⬭   ⬭   ⬭

2 Which is true?

⬭   The biggest share of the shape is yellow.

⬭   Each equal share is a half of the rectangle.

⬭   Each equal share is a quarter of the rectangle.

3 These whole circles
are the same size.
Which is bigger, a fourth
of the whole circle or
a half of the whole circle?

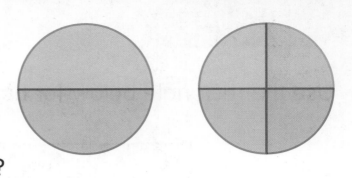

A _____ of the whole circle is bigger

than a _____ of the whole circle.

4 SHOW Draw lines to cut each shape into halves.

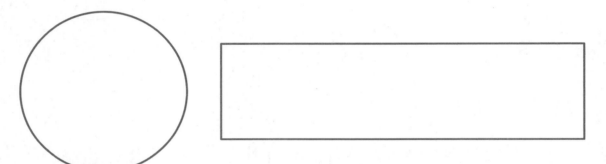

Draw lines to cut each shape into fourths.

1 Which of these shapes is a triangle?

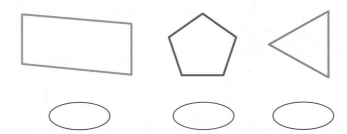

....

2 Which of these shapes has 4 corners?

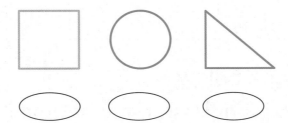

....

3 This shape is a rectangle.

Which is true about all rectangles?

◯ All rectangles have a side that faces straight up.

◯ All rectangles are red.

◯ All rectangles have 4 sides.

4 Draw a triangle.

---

5 Which flat shape below
can you make with these three shapes?

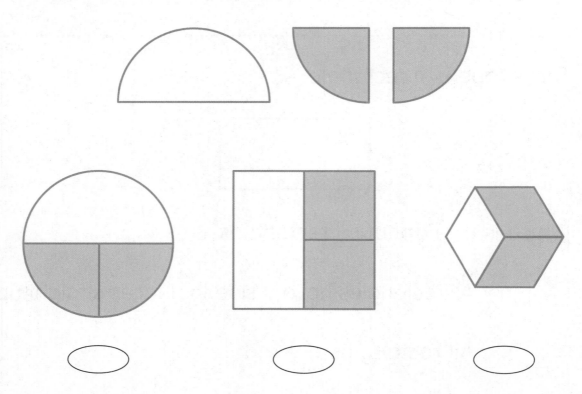

6 Which solid shape below can you make with this group of cubes?

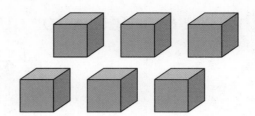

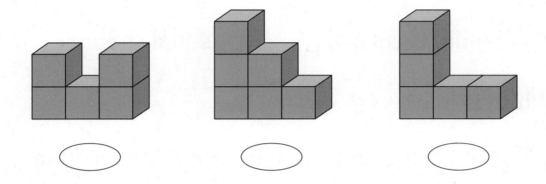

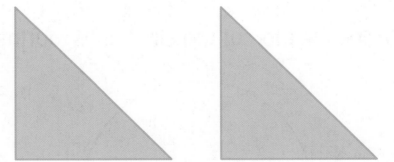

7 DRAW How many flat shapes can you make with the two triangles? Draw them.

Use the square below for questions 8 and 9.

8 The square is cut into _____ equal shares.

9 Which is true?

◯ Each equal share is a half of the square.

◯ Each equal share is a fourth of the square.

◯ Each equal share is bigger than the square.

10 SHOW Draw lines to cut the circle into fourths.

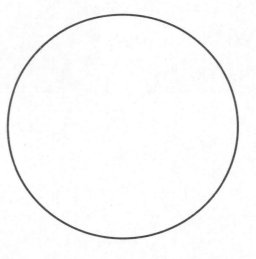

A SQUARE PUZZLE

1 Draw a line to cut the big square into halves. What shapes did you make? _____

2 Draw another line to cut the big square into fourths. What shapes did you make? _____

3 Color one of the small shapes you made. Draw lines to cut the shape you colored into fourths. _____

4 Count all the shapes—big and small. How many shapes are there in all? _____

5 What is another way you could have drawn a line to cut the big square into halves?

Talk about it.

Glossary

add to find how many in all (Lesson I)

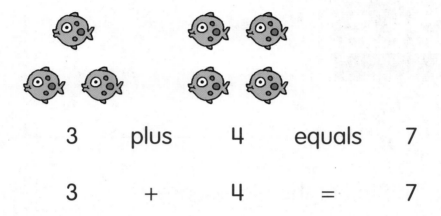

3	plus	4	equals	7
3	+	4	=	7

addends the numbers you add (Lesson 5)

$$3 \leftarrow \text{addend}$$
$$\underline{+\ 2} \leftarrow \text{addend}$$
$$5$$

clock (Lesson 20)

closed shape (Lesson 22)

closed

count on (Lesson 6)

5 + 3 = 8

5   →   6   7   8

data information (Lesson 21)

doubles (Lesson 7)

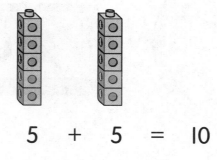

5 + 5 = 10

doubles plus 1 (Lesson 7)

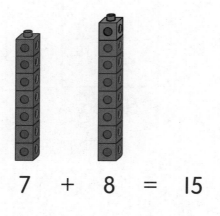

7 + 8 = 15

equal shares (Lesson 24)

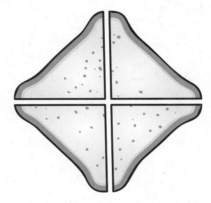

The sandwich has 4 equal shares.

equal sign (=) (Lesson 9)

$$7 + 4 = 11$$

↑

equal sign

equal to (=) (Lesson 14)

$$22 = 22$$

↑

is equal to

equation a number sentence with an
equal sign (Lesson 9)

$$4 + 6 = 10$$

$$9 - 2 = 7$$

$$5 + 3 = 3 + 5$$

face (Lesson 23)

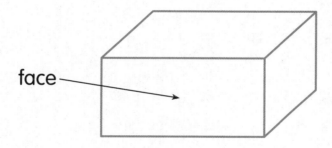

face

flat shape (Lesson 23)

fourths (or **quarters**) (Lesson 24)

This pizza is in fourths.

greater than (>) (Lesson 14)

$$22 > 16$$

is greater than

half (halves) (Lesson 24)

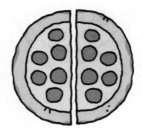

This pizza is in halves.

half hour (Lesson 20)

There are 30 minutes in a half hour.

hour (Lesson 20)

There are 60 minutes in 1 hour.

hour hand (Lesson 20)

hour hand

hundred chart (Lesson 11)

1	2	3	4	5	6	7	8	9	10
11	12	13	14	15	16	17	18	19	20
21	22	23	24	25	26	27	28	29	30
31	32	33	34	35	36	37	38	39	40
41	42	43	44	45	46	47	48	49	50
51	52	53	54	55	56	57	58	59	60
61	62	63	64	65	66	67	68	69	70
71	72	73	74	75	76	77	78	79	80
81	82	83	84	85	86	87	88	89	90
91	92	93	94	95	96	97	98	99	100

length (Lesson 18)

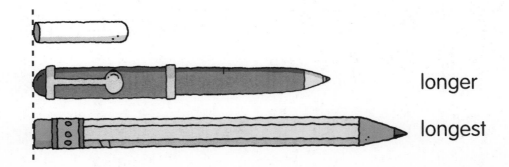

longer

longest

less than (<) (Lesson 14)

$$16 < 22$$

↑

is less than

 M

minute (Lesson 20)

There are 60 minutes in 1 hour.

minute hand (Lesson 20)

minute hand

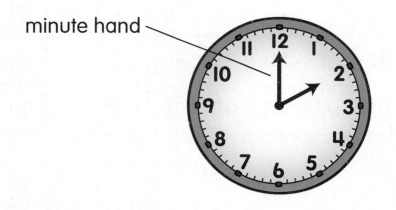

 N

number name a number in words (Lesson 12)

14 = fourteen

ones (Lesson 13)

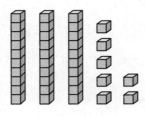

37 has 7 ones.

open shape (Lesson 22)

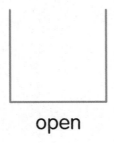

open

related facts facts that have the same numbers
(Lesson 5)

$$6 + 5 = 11$$
$$5 + 6 = 11$$
$$11 - 5 = 6$$
$$11 - 6 = 5$$

side (Lesson 22)

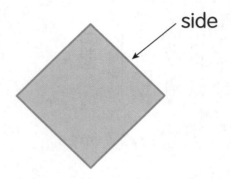

side

solid shape (Lesson 23)

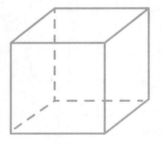
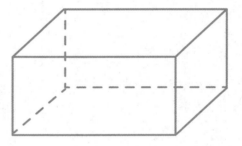

square (Lesson 22)

subtract to find how many are left (Lessons 2, 6)

9	minus	3	equals	6
9	−	3	=	6

subtraction sentence (Lesson 6)

9 − 6 = 3

sum the answer in addition (Lesson 4)

6 + 5 = 11

↑

sum

table (Lesson 21)

Weather

sunny		⦀⦀⦀⦀
rain		|||
snow		||

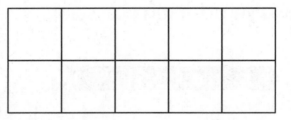

tally marks (Lesson 21)

| stands for 1.   ⦀⦀⦀ stands for 5.

ten frame (Lesson 8)

tens (Lesson 13)

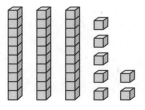

37 has 3 tens.

tens and ones chart (Lesson 13)

Tens	Ones

time (Lesson 20)

The time is 4:30.

triangle (Lesson 22)

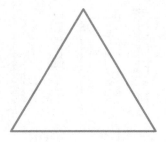

unit (Lesson 19)

You can measure lengths with units.

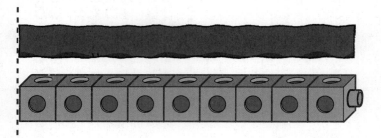

9 units long

Math Tool: Hundred Chart

1	2	3	4	5	6	7	8	9	10
11	12	13	14	15	16	17	18	19	20
21	22	23	24	25	26	27	28	29	30
31	32	33	34	35	36	37	38	39	40
41	42	43	44	45	46	47	48	49	50
51	52	53	54	55	56	57	58	59	60
61	62	63	64	65	66	67	68	69	70
71	72	73	74	75	76	77	78	79	80
81	82	83	84	85	86	87	88	89	90
91	92	93	94	95	96	97	98	99	100

Name _____

Math Tool: Clocks

Name _____

Math Tool: Digital Clocks

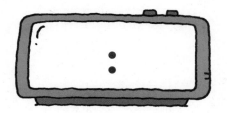

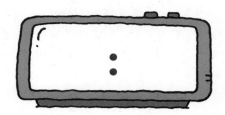

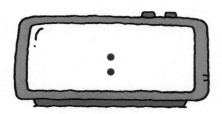

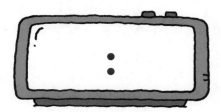

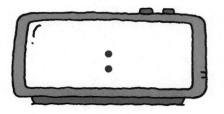

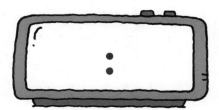

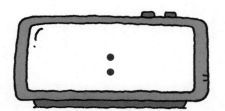

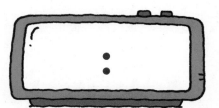

Name _____

Math Tool: Ten Frame

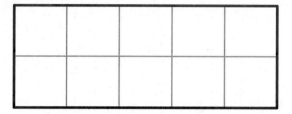

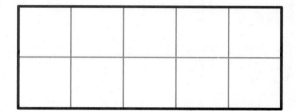

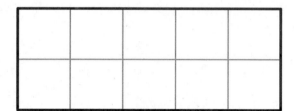

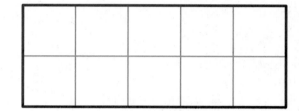

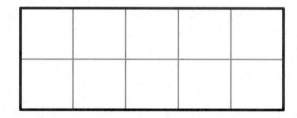

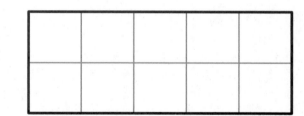

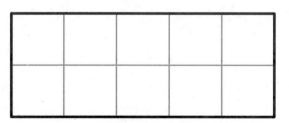

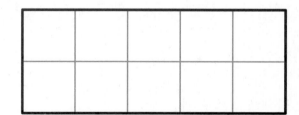

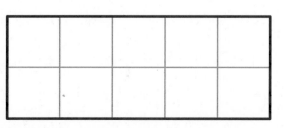

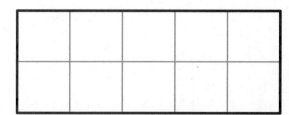

Math Tool: Tens and Ones Chart

Tens	Ones

Tens	Ones

Tens	Ones

Tens	Ones

Tens	Ones

Tens	Ones

Tens	Ones

Tens	Ones

Notes

Notes

Notes

Notes